Developing Hi

UNDERSTANDING AND INTERPRETING THE PAST

Ages
5-6

Anita Loughrey

A & C BLACK

Contents

Published 2007 by A & C Black Publishers Limited
38 Soho Square, London W1D 3HB
www.acblack.com

ISBN 978-0-7136-8395-0

Copyright text and illustrations © Bender Richardson White
Copyright cover illustration © Sholto Walker
Project managers: Lionel Bender and Ben White
Editors: Lucy Poddington and Deborah Kespert
Design: Susan McIntyre
Illustrator: Moreno Chiaccheria
The publishers thank Rick Weights and Alf Wilkinson of the Historical Association for their educational advice.

A CIP catalogue record for this book is available from the British Library.

Printed in Great Britain by Martins the Printers, Berwick-on-Tweed.

This book is produced using paper that is made from wood grown in managed, sustainable forests. It is natural, renewable and recyclable. The logging and manufacturing processes conform to the environmental regulations of the country of origin.

Introduction

Developing History is a series of seven photocopiable activity books for history lessons. Each book provides a range of activities that not only develop children's knowledge and understanding of events, people and changes in the past, but also provide opportunities to develop their investigative and interpretive skills.

The activities vary in their approach. Some are based on first-hand observations, some present text and images for the children to analyse, and others require the children to find information from books and electronic sources. They focus on questioning, observing, generating thoughts and ideas, planning, carrying out investigations, recording findings, checking and questioning findings and presenting explanations. The activities include independent and group work.

The activities in **Developing History: Ages 5–6** are based on the QCA schemes of work for history at Key Stage 1 and support children's development in the following areas from the programme of study:
• Place events and objects in chronological order
• Use common words and phrases relating to the passing
   of time
• Recognise why people did things, why events happened and
   what happened as a result
• Identify differences between ways of life at different times
• Identify different ways in which the past is represented
• Find out about the past from a range of sources
   of information
• Ask and answer questions about the past
• Communicate in a variety of ways.

The activities are linked with other areas of the curriculum where appropriate.

Each activity specifies the learning outcome and features a **Teachers' note** at the foot of the page, which may be masked before photocopying. This will flag any resources needed for the activity. Expanded teaching notes are also provided in the **Notes on the activities** on pages 5–12. This section gives further information and provides key vocabulary to work through at the start of each activity.

Most of the activity sheets end with a challenge (**Now try this!**) which reinforces and extends the children's learning and provides the teacher with an opportunity for assessment. These activities might be appropriate for only a few children; it is not expected that the whole class should complete them. A separate sheet of paper will be needed for some of the extension activities.

Most children will be able to carry out the activities independently. It is not expected that the children will be able to read all the instructions on the sheets, but that someone will read with them. Children gradually become accustomed to seeing instructions, and learn their purpose long before they can read them.

Organisation and resources

Most activities require few resources beyond pencils and general classroom items, including spare paper on occasion. However, because the Programme of Study for History require the use of primary source materials and the examination of objects from the time being studied (not just drawings of these objects), there will be times when children will need additional resources. They may need to have access to books, CD-ROMs, DVDs or to computers to search the Internet for images and information. These occasions will be pointed out in the **Teachers' note**. You may want to use electronic interactive whiteboards or overhead projectors to display activity sheets or source material.

Ensure you have a simple class timeline to help the children place the period in its chronological context. The timeline helps them to meet the requirements to place events, people and changes into the correct periods of time and to use dates and vocabulary related to the passing of time. Clearly mark the direction in which to move along the timeline. It would also be useful to have a chart on the wall listing months and days and to make word cards showing suitable adjectives and picture cards to give a visual impression of artefacts. You will also find it helpful to build up your own resource bank of books (including picture books and story books about the various study units), posters, newspapers and old photographs, especially of your local area or historic sites you and your class may visit.

Structure of a history lesson

To get the best use of the activity sheets, gather all the resources you need before the lesson. Spend 10 to 15 minutes discussing the activity and making sure all the children understand what they have to do and how they will achieve it. Give the children about 20 minutes on the activity. Allow 5 to 10 minutes for whole-class review and consolidation.

Useful websites

You can find information and pictures relating to the topics in this book on the following websites:

www.abcgallery.com

www.museumofchildhood.org.uk

www.punchandjudy.com

www.ancientegypt.co.uk

www.bbc.co.uk/history

www.ssgreatbritain.org

www.guy-fawkes.com

www.gunpowder-plot.org

.

Notes on the activities

The notes below expand upon those provided at the foot of the activity pages. They give ideas for making the most of the activity sheet, including suggestions for the whole-class introduction and discussion or for follow-up work. To help teachers to select appropriate learning experiences for their pupils, the activities are grouped into sections within each book, but the pages need not be presented in the order in which they appear unless stated otherwise.

All about us

This was me (page 12) focuses on the way the children have changed over time. Emphasise the visual differences such as they have grown bigger, their hair may be different and their faces may look thinner. Invite them to show the class their photos and encourage them to talk about the changes they notice. Provide an opportunity for them to discuss significant memories and achievements. Ask the children if they will keep on growing bigger as they get older. Introduce the idea that older people are not always taller than younger people. Link this work with science (Ourselves, growing and changing, and growing older).

Vocabulary: *baby, toddler, then, now, younger, timeline.*

Now I can... (page 13) encourages the children to make observations about their own abilities. Investigate the things they can do now and compare with what they were able to do in the past. Emphasise as they get older people are able to do more things, such as sit up, talk, walk and run. Explain this is because their bodies have grown stronger and their brains have become more developed. If possible, ask a visitor to bring a baby into class and talk to the children about the things the baby can and cannot do. This activity can be linked with work in science (Ourselves, growing and changing, and growing older).

Vocabulary: *baby, toddler, then, now, past, present, future, today, yesterday, tomorrow.*

My family tree (page 14) looks at different family generations to provide children with the opportunity to explore the passing of time within their own family. This activity should be approached sensitively. Some children may be able to tell you about great-grandparents. The activity could be introduced by looking at famous families, such as the royal family, and identifying the different generations. If the children do not have photos of themselves, pictures could be taken with a school digital camera and printed out for the children to cut and paste onto their activity sheet. This activity could also be linked with science (Ourselves, differences between humans).

Vocabulary: *generation, parents, grandparents, family tree, brother, sister, aunt, uncle.*

Generation game: 1 and 2 (pages 15–16) helps to develop the children's understanding of growth and how they are able to do more things as they get older. The game focuses on the kinds of things babies and toddlers can do, so the children are able to discuss and relate the activities shown on the gameboard to experiences within their own childhood. They may also be able to discuss things they have observed younger siblings or friends achieve. The game can be linked with work in numeracy (Counting and understanding number, read numerals from 1 to 20; Calculating, count on and back in ones, twos and threes).

Vocabulary: *numbers 1–20, generation, forwards, backwards, start, finish.*

The activity on **Class birthdays** (page 17) provides opportunities for the children to explore time-related vocabulary. Introduce the activity sheet by chanting the months and talking about seasonal differences in relation to each month. Have a list of the months displayed in the classroom, preferably with visual clues, and point to the corresponding month as you say its name to reinforce understanding and word recognition. The chart can be modelled as a whole class activity in the plenary by using a copy on an overhead projector or electronic whiteboard. Ask the children to stand up as you call out each month, if that is the month of their birthday. Count the children and colour in the corresponding squares. The children can then check the results against their own graphs. This activity links to core learning in mathematics (Handling data).

Vocabulary: *birthday, class, month, year, January, February, March, April, May, June, July, August, September, October, November, December, youngest, oldest, before, after.*

Our family traditions (page 18) allows the children to explore different family traditions from their own and other cultures. Add any other traditions that you feel are relevant to your particular class and children. Explain to the children how some families celebrate name days, when they have been named after a particular saint, rather than birthdays. If possible arrange for someone to speak to the class about their name day, or one or more of the traditions from the word bank, and how they celebrate it. Allow children to add their own family traditions and special events not on the list. This activity supports work in citizenship (Living in a diverse world).

Vocabulary: *tradition, celebrate, celebrate, month, year, birthday, anniversary, Hanukkah, Ramadan, Halloween, Bonfire Night, Hogmanay, Easter, Christmas.*

Investigating daily life

My typical day (page 19) can be introduced by using a large clock and moving the hands through each hour. Ask the children to suggest what they would normally be doing at these times. Draw pictures to illustrate their suggestions on the board. Repeat the activity for half past the hour. If possible, give each child a smaller clock face, to allow them to move the hands themselves. Ask questions like: what time of the day would you eat breakfast, what time of the day would you eat lunch, what time do you go to bed, what time do you get home from school, etc. Let all the children move the hands on their clock faces and hold them up in answer to each question. Ask them what their favourite time of the day is and encourage them to tell you why. This activity has curriculum links with mathematics (Measuring).

Vocabulary: *am, morning, pm, afternoon, evening, before, after, day, night, o'clock, half past.*

Questionnaire (page 20) concentrates on what schools were like in the past. It can be used as a homework activity to take home and interview parents or grandparents or as example questions the children could use to interview a visitor. Emphasise that this is one method of finding information about the past. Tell them historians also use photographs, old newspapers and diaries. Suggest that the children tape record their interview. The recordings could later be transcribed and their findings recorded in a word-processing document. Discuss with the children other questions they might ask to find out more about what schools were like in the past. Provide time for the children to play back or report to the class what they found out from their interview. The activity supports core learning in literacy (Listening and responding).

Vocabulary: *questionnaire, evidence, year, school, uniform, lesson, best, worst, school dinners, past.*

Fresh food (page 21) investigates how people kept their food fresh before refrigerators were invented. Emphasise that food is a basic requirement of life. Ask the children what types of food they like and dislike; what meals they eat during the day and what times these meals are usually eaten. Look at pictures of historical kitchen artefacts, identify them and describe their purpose. It may be possible to borrow items from the local museum service. Methods available for preserving food included drying in the sun or wind (for berries, fruit, vegetables and meat), using salt (for meat) and pickling vegetables and eggs. These methods changed the taste and texture of the food. Preserving food by lowering its temperature – chilling or freezing – extended the time for which food items could be stored. Food was often kept cool in the cellar or pantry, or by storing underwater, or lowering down a deep, dark well. This page can be linked to work in science (Ourselves, eating and drinking).

Vocabulary: *refrigerator, ice, salt, pickle, cellar, pantry, underwater, well.*

Money: 1 and 2 (pages 22–23) explores pre-decimal coins. Look at new and old coins in the classroom. Compare the coins on the activity sheet with present-day money. If possible, show some real old coins to the class as well. Children can draw, stick on or make rubbings of old and new coins in two columns, past and present. Explain to the children that the UK moved to decimal money in 1971. Sing nursery rhymes such as *Five Sticky Buns in a Baker's Shop, Hot Cross Buns, Sing a Song of Sixpence, There was a Crooked Man, Half a Pound of Tuppenny Rice, Simple Simon, See Saw, Marjorie Daw*. Show the corresponding money mentioned in the rhymes. Encourage the children to act out some of the rhymes with the cardboard money. The money could also be used for role-play in a class shop or post office. The activity sheets can be adapted to make coin snap cards or money dominoes to reinforce recognition of the coins. The money activities meet the requirements of core learning in mathematics (Measuring).

Vocabulary: *pre-decimal, 1971, guinea, sovereign, crown, half a crown, florin, shilling, sixpence, threepence, old one penny, halfpenny, farthing.*

Transport: 1 and 2 (pages 24–25) focuses on the chronology of different methods of transport and their evolution in the UK. Brainstorm the various forms of transport the children have used, from roller blades, bicycles and scooters to helicopters and jet skis. Make a list of the different methods of transport suggested by the children. It is important to explain that the modes of transport shown on the activity sheet may still be in use in the UK, such as the horse and cart, but we are looking historically at when they were first introduced. On this basis the order is: horse and cart, trains (1850 onwards), buses (1885 onwards), trams (1900s–1950s), cars (1930s onwards) and aeroplanes (1950s onwards). This activity sheet could also be used in conjunction with the activity sheets on seaside holidays. Explain that transport has had a dramatic impact on family leisure and travel. Seaside holidays became more popular with the invention of cars and railways. A questionnaire could be devised to interview parents, grandparents or a class visitor about the type of transport they used as a child. Encourage the children to suggest suitable questions. Interviews can be recorded onto tape. The children could work in small groups to explore a method of transport in more depth and a much more detailed timeline could be produced for display in the classroom. This could be extended as a mini topic for homework or research activity. This activity links to core learning in literacy (Listening and responding).

Vocabulary: *past, present, before, after, old, new, young, recent, modern, long ago.*

How are our toys different from those of the past?

For **Toy timeline** (page 26) ask the children to bring a favourite toy to school. Encourage them to describe the characteristics of their toy using adjectives. List the adjectives they suggest. The children should then draw and label their toy and write a description of it. Have a selection of toys available in the classroom for children who are unable to bring one from home. Ask if they played with different toys when they were younger. How were these toys different from the ones they play with today? Use a collection of class toys to demonstrate which toys would be suitable toys for different ages. Put them in order and label them. The children can make their own toy timeline by drawing toys within their own personal experience. The page and activities can be linked to work in mathematics (Measuring).

Vocabulary: *timeline, modern, new, today, past, present, future, adjective, catalogue.*

Modern or old-fashioned? (page 27) looks at similarities and differences between toys today and toys in the past to reinforce the concepts of 'old' and 'new'. The cards could be sorted into hoops looped together like a Venn diagram. This could then be followed up using real toys from a class collection, placing the toy into the correct hoop. Encourage the children to think of the difference between old when something is broken and old as when it was made a long time ago. Remember that some old-fashioned-looking toys may have been made recently. If possible, supplement the class collection with a selection of toys from the local museum's loan service and use pictures of old toys as visual sources. Ask the children how the toys are different from today and to describe them using adjectives. List the words the children suggest. These adjectives could be made into word cards, so the children can physically label the toys by placing the word card next to it. Encourage them to tell a toy's story. Who did it belong to? Has it had any adventures? The children could write their own storyboard of the toy's adventures for display in the classroom. Help the children to generalise how we know a toy is old. This activity supports work in literacy (Speaking).

> **Vocabulary:** *modern, new, old, old-fashioned, before, after, adjective, dirty, clean, rusty, broken.*

Playtime then and now (page 28) focuses on outdoor toys. The children should begin to distinguish between the styles of old and more modern outside toys. Discuss why roller skates, skateboards and bicycles are not shown in the picture on the activity sheet. Emphasise how toys have changed with the invention of new ideas and materials. Compare the toys and games on the activity sheet to the well-known street scene painting *Children's Games* by Pieter Breughel the Elder (1560). This can be found on the Internet at www.abcgallery.com. An old-fashioned toy shop could be set up as a role-play area. The children could use the old money from pages 22–23 to buy toys from the toy shop. This activity supports work in literacy (Drama) and numeracy (Measuring).

> **Vocabulary:** *olden days, nowadays, past, present, today, yesterday, long ago.*

How toys have changed (page 29) encourages the children to compare old and new toys. Invite the children to bring a teddy bear to school. Group the bears in order of newest to oldest. Label the groups. Discuss how they know which is the oldest and which is the newest. Ask the children to list any toys that have come from films, books or TV shows. The children could make adverts in small groups to merchandise their bears or toys in the toy shop role-play area. Ask the children if different materials have been used to make the teddy bears. Encourage them to identify the materials used. What signs of wear can they observe? Look at the way the bears move and see if the children notice any differences. Point out how some bears have joints. Look at the bears' faces and the materials used on them. This activity links to work in science (Sorting and using materials).

> **Vocabulary:** *old, new, newer, older, modern, label.*

Museum visit (page 30) investigates how toys are classified in museums. Explain that they could be classified by age, e.g. Roman, Tudor, Victorian. Or they could be classified by type, e.g. teddies, dolls, cars, musical toys, or they could be classified by what they are made of, e.g. wood, metal, plastic. The activity sheet can be used on a school trip to a museum that specialises in toys but could be easily adapted for other exhibits by changing the headings. It is possible to use other sources to find out about toys from the past, such as a CD-ROM or an online toy museum, such as www.museumofchildhood.org.uk. Talk about how the toys are displayed. If possible make your own class museum and explore different ways of organising the exhibits.

Make a three-dimensional timeline by arranging toys on a shelf or table. Label the exhibits, make a pictorial guidebook and give visitors guided tours. This links with work in science (Sorting and using materials).

> **Vocabulary:** *classify, chart, museum, exhibit, artefact, age, type, materials, captions.*

Snakes and ladders (page 31) is an example of a game from Victorian times that is still popular today. Snakes and ladders was originally based on a game from India and brought to Britain in 1870 by John Jacques of Jacques of London. The children should take turns to shake the dice and move their counter the appropriate number of squares. Explain the rules to the children and ensure they all understand they go up the ladders and down the snakes. This activity supports work in numeracy (Counting and understanding number).

> **Vocabulary:** *board games, Victorian, year, invent.*

Survey (page 32) provides opportunities for pupils to develop their speaking and listening skills. Ask the children to suggest people they could ask to tell them about old toys. The sheet is designed to be used as an activity to take home and interview their parents or grandparents. Or it can be used to interview a visitor to the class who has offered to talk about toys they played with when they were a child. The children could tape-record their interview and the recordings could later be transcribed and their findings recorded. Provide time for the children to play back or report to the class what they found out from their interview. This activity sheet can be used for literacy (Listening and responding).

> **Vocabulary:** *questions, answers, interview, evidence, record, different, similar.*

What were homes like a long time ago?

This is my home (page 33) prompts children to describe and talk about their own home. Emphasise that people live in different sorts of homes. Ask the children if their home has a garage, a driveway, or double glazing. Encourage the children to recognise the differences between the six different homes featured on the activity sheet. Display large pictures of the various types of homes and point to each one as you speak about them. Encourage them to think why people live in different sorts of homes, e.g. elderly people prefer not to have stairs. If possible, use Google Earth for the children to zoom in on the school and surrounding area using their postcode. The activity meets the requirements of core learning in literacy (Speaking) and geography (Around our school – the local area).

> **Vocabulary:** *caravan, terraced, semi-detached, bungalow, flat, detached, label.*

Looking at houses (page 34) helps children to recognise common external features of domestic dwellings and to record their observations appropriately. Take the children to look at homes near the school. Help them to recognise common features by asking them to look for what is different and what is the same about the homes. Encourage them to talk about what the homes are made from. Ask: what is the roof made from? What is the chimney made from? This activity provides opportunities to make links with the geography schemes of work (Around our school – the local area), the design and technology schemes of work (Homes) and the science schemes of work (Sorting and using materials).

> **Vocabulary:** *door, window, chimney, roof, window sill, letter box, bricks, tiles, thatch, glass, porch, garage, extension, conservatory, label.*

Houses long ago (page 35) identifies key features of a home built a long time ago. The sheet could be introduced to the class by reading the story of the *Three Little Pigs* and discussing the materials the pigs used to build their homes. Encourage the children to think about what their own house is made from. What are the windows made of? What are the doors made of? Ask the children whether these materials were available a long time ago. Look at the picture of the Edwardian home on the activity sheet. Using the knowledge they have developed from activity sheets earlier in this section, ask the children to identify key features they can see. What is different in this home from a modern home? Is it made from the same materials? This activity can be used to support work in science (Sorting and using materials).

> **Vocabulary:** *change, materials, Edwardian, features, door, window, chimney, roof.*

The way things were (page 36) looks at the types of things we would find in people's homes a long time ago. The children are required to draw the corresponding item we use today. For example, for the bed pan they could draw a toilet, for a bed-warmer they should draw a hot water bottle, for the jug and bowl they would draw a sink with taps, and for the gramophone they could draw a CD-player. An idea for display would be to make a large picture of an Edwardian-style house like the inside of dolls house, which fills the display board with three floors and an attic space. Small groups of children could be allocated a room and either: print pictures of appropriate period furniture from the Internet, or copy furniture from books and stick them into the correct room. Encourage the children to describe the objects. This activity sheet supports work in Design and Technology (Homes).

> **Vocabulary:** *old-fashioned, household objects, label, long ago, bed pan, bed-warmer, jug, bowl, gramophone.*

Roman baths (page 37) concentrates on the Romans to explore ways of life of people in the more distant past. The following information can be read to the children to help them understand how Roman baths were different to bathing today. Roman baths were similar to leisure centres. They were large buildings with hot and cold pools, towels, steam rooms, exercise rooms, an arena and hair-cutting salons. There were also reading rooms, libraries, gardens and toilets. Originally, they were only for men but later women had separate rooms added. The Romans would go through the baths in order. They started in the changing rooms where they had oil rubbed onto their skin before going to exercise in one of the exercise courtyards. From here they would move to the warm room where they would laze around in warm water chatting with their friends whilst attendants served them snacks and drinks and scraped their skin. Next they would go to the hot room to build up a sweat again, followed by a quick dip in the cold bath. After this, they would go for a swim in the pool and then enjoy a massage where oils and perfumes were rubbed into their skin. Link to work in literacy (Understanding and interpreting texts).

> **Vocabulary:** *Roman bath, changing room, exercise courtyard, warm room, hot room, cold bath, swimming pool.*

Use the activity sheets **Pairs: 1 and 2** (pages 38–39) to help the children to make inferences about household objects used a long time ago. Provide opportunities for the children to examine Victorian or Edwardian household objects. It may be possible to borrow items from the local museum service. Using one of the objects, work with the children to develop a set of questions to ask. Is it heavy or light? Has it been painted? Is it decorated? What is it made of? What is it? How do we know it is old? What was it used for? Where would it be used? What do we use today? Discuss with the children how the objects would have been used, e.g. a flat iron needed to be heated on a stove before being used to iron. Look at the pictures page 38 and see if the children can identify any of the objects shown before they cut them out and play the games. These games meet the requirements of core learning in literacy (Speaking) and science (Ourselves).

> **Vocabulary:** *flat iron, washboard, carpet beater, cauldron, water pump, gas lamp, fireplace, candle, copper kettle, range, wooden tub, chamber pot.*

A day in Victorian life: 1 and 2 (pages 40–41) requires the children to apply their knowledge and understanding of home life a long time ago. Talk to the children about what it would be like to live in the past. Set up a home corner of a Victorian room with Victorian artefacts for the children to role-play what it would be like to live in Victorian times. Deal out the cards and encourage the children to stay in role, perhaps incorporating some of the items on page 38. Encourage them to take turns being the characters shown on the cards. The children should think of the routine of the day and how some things would be done at specific times, such as the maid preparing the beds, the cook making the food, etc. Let the children take it in turns to sit in the hot seat and the other children ask questions about what it might have been like to live over 100 years ago. Allow them to choose one of the characters they have role-played and write a diary entry. Emphasise how the day has been split into morning, afternoon and evening and brainstorm what each character would do at these times. This activity supports core learning in literacy (Drama).

> **Vocabulary:** *past, Victorian, servant, role-play, character, before, after, long ago, morning, afternoon, evening.*

What were seaside holidays like in the past?

Holidays today (page 42) encourages the children to investigate holidays. Talk about school and other holidays. Sequence the major holidays on a timeline. Encourage the children to identify relationships between holidays and religious festivals, and think about the reasons we have holidays and what happens during different holidays. If possible, use Google Earth and let the children zoom in on some of the popular seaside resorts they have visited by typing in the town name. Try to identify the beach, the pier, the promenade, bathers, sealife centre and fairground at the various resorts children have visited. Barry Island, Blackpool and Bournemouth are good examples to investigate. This activity meets the requirements of geography (Going to the seaside) and can be linked to work in religious education (Beliefs and practice).

> **Vocabulary:** *seaside, sand, cliff, shingle, windbreak.*

Holiday snaps (page 43) provides the children with an opportunity to find out about holidays in the past using photograph-like pictures. Before the session a letter could be sent home asking parents and grandparents if they have any photographs of themselves on holiday at a British seaside when they were younger. These photos could be used for display and compared to the pictures on the sheet. This activity could be extended to look at seaside resorts abroad using tourist brochures from the travel agents. Ask the children to identify and list the natural physical features of seaside holidays, such as the sea, sand, rocks, etc. and those features that are artificial, such as sunbeds, buckets and spades, boats, etc. This activity compliments the learning goals for geography (Going to the seaside).

> **Vocabulary:** *long ago, past, present, recent, modern, 1980s, 1950s, caption.*

Trip to the sea (page 44) distinguishes between holidays in the recent and more distant past and helps children to recognise that some things change whilst others stay the same. Let the children study and talk about the pictures on the activity sheet with a partner. Ask the children to mime a seaside activity to the class for the others to guess. Tell the children this could be an activity shown on the sheet, or one they have thought of, or had experience of, themselves. List the activities they mime, on a large sheet of paper, under the headings 'past', 'present' or 'both'. Keep this piece of paper to refer back to. This activity supports core learning in literacy (Drama).

> **Vocabulary:** *past, present, both, similar, different.*

In times gone by (page 45) reinforces that some things change whilst others stay the same. Set up a role-play area that could be used for children to act out their own seaside stories both modern and from times gone by. Encourage the children to pretend they are in Victorian times, using information gathered from the previous activity sheet. What sort of activities would children enjoy doing? Refer them to the 'past' column they acted out for the **Trip to the sea** activity sheet. The postcard could then be used to write home about their Victorian seaside holiday and the activities they enjoyed. Explain to the children that the penny black stamp was the world's first official adhesive postage stamp. It was issued on 1 May 1840. The activity sheet supports core learning in literacy (Drama).

> **Vocabulary:** *postcard, stamp, penny black, Victorian.*

Mementoes (page 46) focuses on souvenirs and what they can tell us about seaside holidays in the past. A questionnaire could be made to find out more information about seaside holidays and souvenirs. Brainstorm questions about seaside holidays in the past, which they could ask their parents/carers or grandparents. If possible, ask an elderly person to come into school and give a presentation about their own seaside holidays when they were young. Ask the visitor to bring some old souvenirs to show the class. Discuss what information the souvenirs provide about seaside holidays in the past. This activity matches targets for core learning in literacy (Listening and responding).

> **Vocabulary:** *souvenir, memento, keepsake, reminder, ball, spinning top, cricket bat, yacht, ship in bottle, skipping rope, shell, rock, flag, hoop.*

Punch and Judy (page 47) examines in more detail a particular historical aspect of seaside holidays. If possible, take the children to see a Punch and Judy show or invite Punch and Judy performers to visit the school and talk about the history of Punch and Judy from marionette to hand-puppet and how the story has developed over the years. During the 1800's, Punch and Judy shows were a familiar sight on street corners with the puppeteers making a living by collecting pennies from the audience. When the railways took town crowds to the seasides, Punch went too. More information about the history of the Punch and Judy show can be found at the website www.punchandjudy.com. Use the activity sheet as a visual aid to help the children write and illustrate their own Punch and Judy storylines. They could act out their stories using their own puppets. This activity can be used to meet the requirements of core learning in literacy (Listening and responding).

> **Vocabulary:** *character, puppet, story, act, Punch, Judy, baby, crocodile, theatre.*

Investigating famous people from the past

Super-fan facts (page 48) prompts children to think about what the word 'famous' means. Have a range of pictures from glossy magazines and the Internet, of famous people who are alive and dead. Let the children look at these pictures and talk about them in small groups. Why are these people famous? What people from the past do the children know who are famous? What did they do to become famous? This activity meets the requirements of core learning in literacy (Group discussion and interaction).

> **Vocabulary:** *famous, celebrity, well-known, star, fact.*

The **Pocahontas** activity sheet (page 49) outlines the main events in Pocahontas's life. Explain that Pocahontas was 12 years old when the settlers arrived and 20 years old when she met King James I. She died soon after. Encourage the children to retell the story in small groups. The children could act out these main events using voices for characters. When Pocahontas went to England she would have worn European-style clothing. An interesting activity would be to compare her native North American dress to the clothes she would have worn in England. Ask the children to look for similarities and differences. The correct order for the sentences is: 3, 6, 7, 4, 8, 1, 2 and 5. The activity supports core learning in literacy (Group discussion and interaction; Speaking).

> **Vocabulary:** *Pocahontas, James I, North American Indian, baptised, settlers.*

The Pocahontas legend (page 50) infers information from John Smith's written account of how he met Pocahontas. He was leading an expedition in December 1607 when North American Indians captured him. According to John Smith, he was grabbed, stretched over two large, flat stones and threatened with clubs. Suddenly, a 12-year-old girl flung herself across his body to save him from death. Her father, Powhatan, declared John Smith a friend and adopted him as his son. Read John Smith's account to the children:

> [A] long consultation was held, but the conclusion was, two great stones were brought before Powhatan: then as many as could laid hands on him, dragged him to them, and thereon laid his head, and being ready with their clubs, to beat out his brains, Pocahontas the King's dearest daughter, when no entreaty would prevail, got his head in her arms, and laid her own upon his to save him from death.

The page meets literacy objectives (Listening and responding) and (Engaging and responding to texts).

> **Vocabulary:** *feast, ritual, ceremony, tribe.*

Sailing to England (page 51) helps children to appreciate that people are famous for their qualities and actions. Discuss how long is the journey to England from North America using a globe. Encourage the children to suggest adjectives that describe people who went on long journeys by boat in those days, e.g. *brave, patient* and *healthy.* Tell the children that Pocahontas was invited to England to meet King James I because of the good deeds she had done helping the British settlers and was given a very warm welcome. Ask the children why they think Pocahontas wanted to help the settlers. The activity could be enhanced by hot-seating where the teacher or other adult pretends they are Pocahontas or King James I and the children ask relevant questions. This activity meets requirements for literacy (Group discussion and interaction).

> **Vocabulary:** *voyage, journey, travel, England, English.*

Tutankhamun (page 52) encourages children to investigate secondary sources to find out information about Tutankhamun and the clothes he wore. Explain to the class that Tutankhamun was only eight years old when he became pharaoh and died when he was about 19. Look at atlases and globes to determine where Egypt is. Ask if the clothes Tutankhamun wore are like kings wear now. How are they different? Talk about the difference in climate. Point out the eye make-up, headdress and elaborately coloured collar around his neck. The activity supports literacy goals (Text structure and organisation).

> **Vocabulary:** *Tutankhamun, research, ancient, Egypt, investigate, pharaoh, royalty.*

Making a mummy (page 53) concentrates on sequencing events with particular reference to mummification. The British Museum website www.ancientegypt.co.uk contains a lot of relevant information that could be used to introduce the activity sheet. The ancient Egyptians developed a method of preserving bodies so they would remain lifelike. The process included embalming the bodies and wrapping them in strips of linen. The body was placed inside two coffins and then a sarcophagus, which was highly decorated with hieroglyphics. The correct order is: 4, 3, 2, and 1. This activity supports literacy early learning goals (Text structure and organisation).

> **Vocabulary:** *mummy, British Museum, ancient Egypt, hieroglyphics, sarcophagus, coffin.*

Uncovering the tomb (page 54) outlines the story of Howard Carter's discovery of Tutankhamun's tomb. Show the children pictures of Egypt and the pyramids. Explain that Egypt is a popular tourist destination but it was such a long and difficult journey in the early 1900s that it was very rare for people from England to go there. Tell them Howard Carter was fascinated by the treasures of ancient Egypt and decided to search for the tomb of the boy king, Tutankhamun. The search was funded by a wealthy Englishman called Lord Carnarvon. Carter searched every winter for five years but found nothing. He was about to give up but persuaded Carnarvon to fund one more try. In 1922, he discovered stairs going underground to a door. Explain that the things we know about Tutankhamun were discovered by historians and archaeologists after studying the treasures found in his tomb. Use large sand trays for children to try their own archaeological dig by carefully unearthing pre-planted pot fragments and other artefacts. Encourage the children to role-play discovering the tomb and to explain how they feel about this great discovery. This activity links to core learning in literacy (Listening and responding; Drama).

> **Vocabulary:** *pharaoh, pyramid, mummification, tomb, before, after, archaeologist, treasure.*

Brunel's achievements (page 55) provides the opportunity to explore and research in more depth the achievements of a famous person. The children could use construction kits to design their own bridges and investigate the principles of the bridges and tunnels Brunel designed. Discuss with the children how Brunel's inventions made a difference to the community then and now. The children can work in small groups to research in more detail one of Brunel's constructions and report back to the class what they discover. This activity contributes to cross-curricular work on art and design (Investigating materials) and citizenship (People who help us).

> **Vocabulary:** *famous, railway, suspension bridge, tunnel, observatory, paddle ship, steamship, construction.*

Brunel's designs (page 56) introduces the children to the steamship SS *Great Britain* and its design. The SS *Great Britain* took four years to build. It was launched in 1843 and was the first propeller-powered ship to cross the Atlantic Ocean. It was the world's first iron-hulled, screw propeller-driven steam-powered passenger liner. It was very successful and remained in service for 30 years, journeying regularly to Australia. It is now on show to the public in Bristol docks. For more information on the SS *Great Britain*, see: www.ssgreatbritain.org. This activity can be linked to work in art and design (Investigating materials).

> **Vocabulary:** *iron hull, screw propeller, steamship, passenger liner, Atlantic Ocean.*

Ships (page 57) looks in more detail at Brunel's designs and how they compare with ships today. Compare pictures of modern ships and cruise liners to the SS *Great Britain.* Ask the children what materials were used then. What materials do people use now? Why? Encourage them to identify new features that have been added to cruise liners today, such as more decks, lifeboats and swimming pools. This activity links to work in art and design (Investigating materials) and science (Sorting and using materials).

> **Vocabulary:** *then, now, steam ship, modern, cruise liner.*

What are we remembering on Bonfire Night?

Guy Fawkes (page 58) encourages children to ask and answer questions about the past. Introduce the activity sheet by teaching the children the rhyme:

> Remember, remember the fifth of November
> The gunpowder treason and plot.
> I see no reason why gunpowder treason
> Should ever be forgot.
> Guy Fawkes, Guy Fawkes, 'twas his intent
> To blow up king and parliament.
> Three score barrels were laid below
> To prove old England's overthrow;
> By God's mercy he was catched
> With a dark lantern and lighted match.
> Holler boys, holler boys, let the bells ring.
> Holler boys, holler boys, God save the King!

The rhyme reminds people why on the 5 November each year, bonfires are lit, often with a guy made of cloth sitting on top. Point out that the king mentioned in the rhyme is King James I, who was the same king who invited Pocahontas to visit from North America. Ask the children to tell the class what they know about Bonfire Night. Re-read the rhyme and ask the children why they think that Guy Fawkes is famous. This activity supports core learning in literacy (Listening and responding) and (Understanding and interpreting texts). It can also be linked to work in art and design (Investigating materials).

> **Vocabulary:** *bonfire, past, very long time ago, parliament, before, after, when, gunpowder, treason, plot.*

The Gunpowder Plot (page 59) requires the children to recount a significant event from the past. The website www.guy-fawkes.com provides background detail on Guy Fawkes and the Gunpowder Plot. Tell them he was part of a plan to kill King James I and his advisors on 5 November 1605 by blowing up the Houses of Parliament. Show the children the date on a timeline. Explain that Guy Fawkes hid in a cellar under the Houses of Parliament with 36 barrels of gunpowder. But the cellars were searched and Guy Fawkes was arrested and taken to the king for questioning. Despite being tortured, he kept quiet but Government spies already knew the plan. Before the children start the activity sheet show them modern pictures of the Houses of Parliament and pictures of what they would have looked like in 1605. This activity supports work in literacy (Understanding and interpreting texts).

> **Vocabulary:** *Guy Fawkes, Gunpowder Plot, plotters, guards, Houses of Parliament, arrest, treason, caption.*

Letter to Lord Monteagle (page 60) focuses on communicating knowledge and understanding of events. It is believed that one of the plotters, Francis Tresham, wrote a letter to his brother-in-law Lord Monteagle on 26 October 1605, warning him not to attend the opening of Parliament. Monteagle immediately took the letter to King James' Secretary of State Robert Cecil who alerted the authorities. Francis Tresham was arrested and taken to the Tower of London. It is recorded that he died there in December 1605, possibly as a result of poisoning, though some historians believe he was allowed to escape. If possible show the children copies of the original letter and a translation into modern English. This activity supports learning goals in literacy (Understanding and interpreting texts; Engaging and responding to texts).

> **Vocabulary:** *letter, parliament, Lord Monteagle, Houses of Parliament, warning, Gunpowder Plot.*

Gunpowder Plot puppets: 1 and 2 (pages 61–62) provides the children with opportunities to explore an important historical event through role-play. Explain that they are going to act out a real event. Introduce the term 'characters' and ask them to name the characters in the story. Discuss what each character might have said and done. Give the children time to role-play the story and then invite each group to perform their version to the class. Encourage the children watching to comment on and praise the performance. Useful website links that outline the events leading up to the plot include www.gunpowder-plot.org. This activity satisfies the objectives for core learning in literacy (Drama).

> **Vocabulary:** *characters, performance, finger puppet, story, act, plotters, guards, King James I.*

Celebration (page 63) looks in detail at how historical events can be commemorated by celebration. On 5 November 1606 people in London lit bonfires to mark the anniversary of the foiling of the plot to kill the king, beginning a tradition which has survived right through to the present day. Another tradition also survives. As part of the ritual at the State Opening of Parliament each year, the Yeomen of the Guard, complete with their Tudor uniforms and armed with pikes, carry out a search of the buildings. Ask the children how they celebrate Bonfire Night. List words they associate with Bonfire Night celebrations. This could be extended to think of onomatopoeic words linked to firework sounds, such as *hiss, bang, pop, zoom*, etc. Discuss any other celebrations they can think of such as Christmas, Easter, Remembrance Day, and ask the children what they commemorate. Compare these celebrations with the family traditions they identified for the activity sheet on page 18). This activity can be linked to Citizenship (Living in a diverse world).

> **Vocabulary:** *celebration, sparklers, toffee, apples, baked potatoes, bonfire, fireworks, commemorate.*

Hero or villain? (page 64) explores the different ways the past can be represented. Ask the children their opinions of Guy Fawkes and whether they thought he was a freedom fighter or a terrorist. Encourage them to give reasons for their answers and list these reasons under two columns 'Hero' and 'Villain'. There is a good interactive game based on the gunpowder plot on the BBC website www.bbc.co.uk/history/british. Explain that Guy Fawkes was not actually burnt on a bonfire but was hung, drawn and quartered. Ask the children if they knew someone was going to do something wrong what might they do. Link this work to citizenship (Choices).

> **Vocabulary:** *past, present, now, then, freedom fighter, terrorist, hero, villain, speech bubble.*

This was me

What did you look like when you were younger? What do you look like now?

- **Draw or stick pictures on the** `timeline` .
- **Write the year of the picture in the box.**

baby	toddler	now

year

year

year

Now try this!

• **Talk about your timeline with a friend.**

Teachers' note Introduce this activity by looking at pictures and photographs of children in mail order catalogues to emphasise different ages. Ask the children to identify visual differences between a baby and a toddler. Encourage them to compare what they looked like as a baby with what they look like now. Stick photographs on the activity sheet or if you prefer they could draw pictures. Some children will need help to work out the year they would have been a toddler.

Developing History Ages 5–6 © A & C BLACK

Now I can...

• **Finish the sentences to show what you could do at different ages.**

baby

First I could _cry, then I_ _____

_____

_____.

toddler

Next I could _____

_____

_____

_____

_____.

five-year-old

Now I can _____

_____

_____

_____

_____

_____.

Now try this!

In the future, I will _____

_____.

Teachers' note Ask the children to identify the things they were able to do when they were a baby and a toddler. Ask them when they first sat up, walked or talked. Encourage them to identify things they are able to do now, which they would not have been able to do when they were a baby, such as do up buttons, hold a pencil and walk to school. Ask them to suggest what they think they will be able to do in the future, such as swim without arm bands or drive a car.

Developing History
Ages 5–6
© A & C BLACK

My family tree

Gain an understanding of the concept of generation

- **Who is part of your** family tree **?**
- **Draw or stick on pictures.**

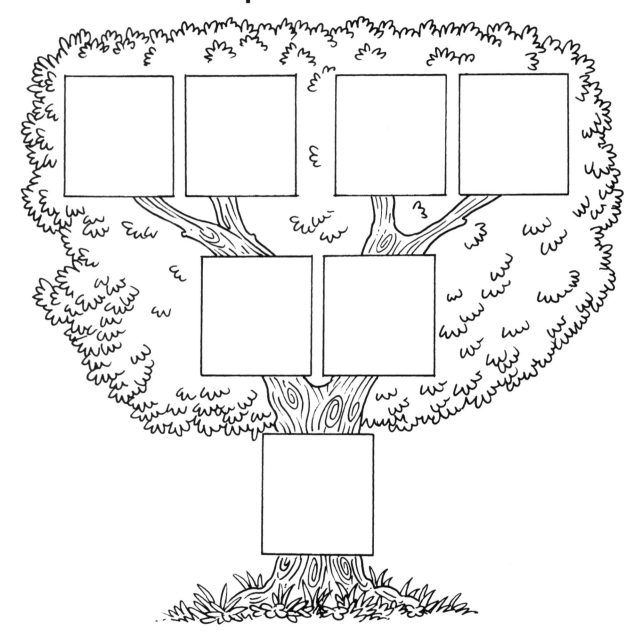

- **Draw in any brothers or sisters.**
- **Talk about your family tree with a partner.**

Teachers' note Enlarge this sheet to A3 on a photocopier. Encourage the children to draw pictures or stick photographs on the family tree to show themselves, their parents and their grandparents. Ask the children to specify who is the oldest and who is the youngest. Explain that a generation includes people born around the same period of time. Tell the children this means that all the children in their class are from the same generation.

**Developing History
Ages 5–6**
© A & C BLACK

This is a game for 2–4 players.

Teachers' note You need one copy of this page and one copy of the rules and spinner on page 16 for each group of up to four children. Copy both sheets onto card. The children should take turns to spin the spinner. Help them to read any words in the space on which they land and act out the activity. The winner is the first to finish the game. Provide opportunities to discuss the process of growing up and being able to do more things for themselves.

Developing History
Ages 5–6
© **A & C BLACK**

15

Generation game: 2

- ## Make the spinner and counters.
- ## Play the board game.

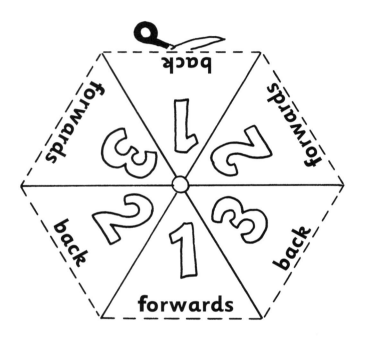

spinner

How to play

* Take turns to spin the spinner.
* When it lands on 'forwards', you can start.
* Use your counter to move forwards the number of spaces shown.
* Then the next player takes a turn.
* Each time you spin, move forwards or back the number shown.
* The winner is the first player to reach the finish.

Colour each counter a different colour.

counters

Teachers' note You need one copy of this page for a group of up to four children. The spinner and counters are designed to be used with the board game on page 15. Copy it onto card and help the children to cut out the spinner and push a cocktail stick through the middle. Read and discuss the rules with the children. Emphasise that they must take turns.

Developing History
Ages 5–6
© **A & C BLACK**

Class birthdays

Use time-related vocabulary

- **Colour a square to show what month your birthday is.**

- **Colour a square for each person in your class to show when their birthday is.**

- **Which month has the most birthdays?**

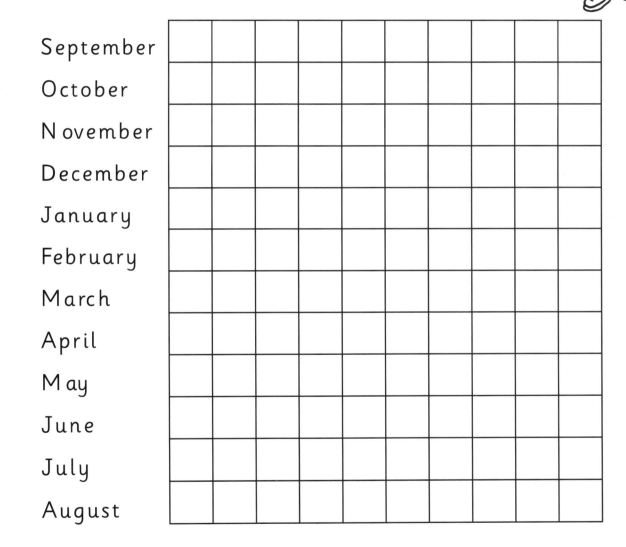

September

October

November

December

January

February

March

April

May

June

July

August

- **Who are the youngest in the class?**
- **Who are the oldest in the class?**

Teachers' note This activity could be done first individually, then in small groups and then as a class. Remember that the oldest children's birthdays will be in September and the youngest children's birthdays will be in August.

Developing History
Ages 5–6
© **A & C BLACK**

Our family traditions

Describe characteristics of family life

Which traditions **do your family celebrate?**

• **Write them on the calendar.**

January	February	March	April
May	June	July	August
September	October	November	December

Word bank

Christmas	Easter	birthday
anniversary	Hanukkah	Ramadan
Halloween	Bonfire night	Hogmanay

Use the word bank to help you.

Now try this!

• **Talk about your calendar with a partner.**

Which traditions are the same?

Which traditions are different?

Teachers' note Read the activity sheet with the children. Ensure they fully understand each family tradition. Some children may need more support identifying which tradition goes with which month. Provide opportunities for the children to share their experiences with the different traditions from the word bank.

**Developing History
Ages 5–6**
© A & C BLACK

My typical day

Use common words and phrases relating to the passing of time

- **Draw what you do at these times of the day.**
- **Write a sentence about each picture.**

Use the word bank to help you.

Word bank	
morning	noon
afternoon	evening
before	after
day	night
o'clock	half past

_____

_____

_____

_____

Now try this!

What is your favourite time of the day?
- **Talk to a friend.**

Teachers' note When the children are familiar with recognising half past and o'clock, ask them to tell you the times on the activity sheet and what they would be doing at these times. More able children can write a sentence to explain what they do at each time.

Developing History
Ages 5–6
© A & C BLACK

Questionnaire

Find out about the past by asking questions

- ## Use these questions to interview someone about their school days.
- ## Add two more questions of your own.

1. What year did you start school?

   _____

2. How did you get to school?

   _____

3. Did you wear a uniform?

   _____

4. What were the school dinners like?

   _____

5. What was your best lesson?

   _____

6. What was your worst lesson?

   _____

7. _____?

   _____

8. _____?

   _____

- ## Tell the class what you found out from your interview.

Teachers' note Read the questions with the children and make sure they all understand that they are going to investigate what schools were like in the past by asking their parents or grandparents. Explain that interviewing people is a widely used method of gathering historical evidence. Ensure they have written their own questions before the sheet is taken home for homework.

Developing History
Ages 5–6
© **A & C BLACK**

How did people keep their food fresh before they had refrigerators?

• Write or draw.

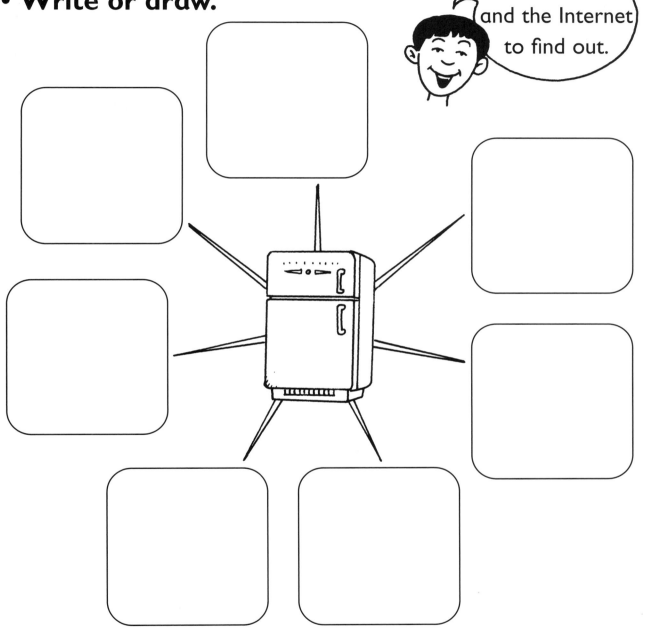

Use books and the Internet to find out.

Now try this!

• For each of your ideas, name a food that could be kept fresh in this way.

Teachers' note Before the lesson begins, ensure you have enough books, websites and pictures of food for the children to study and identify how they would be kept fresh. Before starting the activity sheet discuss ways food is kept fresh at home. Show pictures of different food types such as eggs, bread, meat, fruit and vegetables and ask where they are stored at home. Ask what sort of food was eaten in the past and how these foods were kept fresh. List their ideas.

**Developing History
Ages 5–6**
© A & C BLACK

Money: 1

- ## Colour in the coins.
- ## Cut them out and make them.

Key

sovereign

crown

half crown

florin

shilling

Now try this!

- ## Find out what each coin was made of. Use books and the Internet.

Teachers' note Photocopy both money activity sheets on pages 22 and 23 onto card. Cut the coins out and carefully stick the heads and tails together. Ensure the children can name all the coins shown on the activity sheet. Discuss how much each coin is worth in equivalent money today.

Developing History
Ages 5–6
© A & C BLACK

Money: 2

Find out about the past from a range of sources

• Colour in the coins, cut out and make them.

Key

sixpence

threepence

one penny

halfpenny

farthing

• Find out what each coin was made of. Use books and the Internet.

Teachers' note Photocopy both money activity sheets on pages 22 and 23 onto card. Cut the coins out and carefully stick the heads and tails together. Ensure the children can name all the coins shown on the activity sheet. Discuss how much each coin is worth in equivalent money today.

Developing History
Ages 5–6
© A & C BLACK

Transport: 1

Place events and objects in chronological order

- ## Cut out the pictures.
- ## Stick them on the timeline .

Work with a friend.

horse and cart

train

bus

tram

car

aeroplane

Teachers' note This sheet is designed to be used in conjunction page 25. When the children have ordered the pictures, talk about the overlap between the different methods of transport. Discuss ways in which transport has improved since the horse and cart. Ask the children what they think it would have been like to travel in the different forms of transport. Discuss how each method of transport has changed and improved over time.

Developing History Ages 5–6
© A & C BLACK

Transport: 2

Place events and objects in chronological order

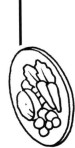

- **Stick the pictures on the timeline to show** oldest **to** newest.

newest

oldest

Now try this!

- **How did the invention of different types of transport affect people?**

Teachers' note The children should work in pairs. Enlarge the timeline onto A3 paper. The children should cut out the different forms of transport on page 24 and stick them in chronological order onto the timeline. Ask which they think is the oldest method of transport and which they think is the newest. Encourage them to give reasons for their suggestions. Point out how transport is improving all the time, e.g. bi-planes to the jumbo jet.

Developing History
Ages 5–6
© **A & C BLACK**

Toy timeline

Find out about aspects of own past

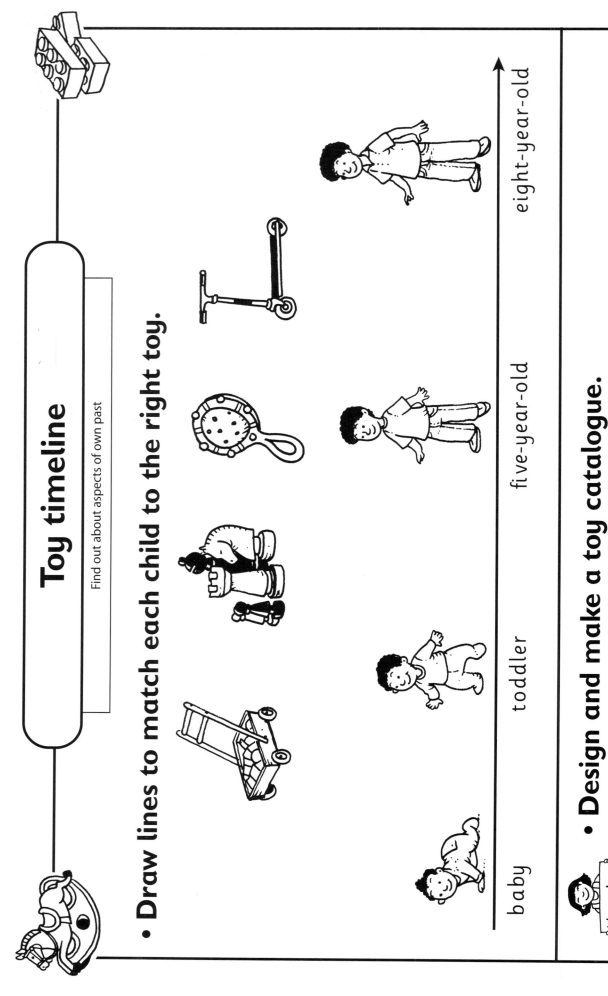

- **Draw lines to match each child to the right toy.**

baby   toddler   five-year-old   eight-year-old

- **Design and make a toy catalogue.**

Now try this!

Teachers' note This timeline goes beyond the children's personal experience. Point out that events on a timeline must be in the right order. The toys can be cut and pasted in the correct order or matched to the corresponding child by drawing a line. Use toy catalogues to emphasise which toys are suitable for which age range. Let the children copy or cut pictures out of the catalogues to make their own toy catalogue in small groups. Encourage them to have at least one toy suitable for each of the children shown on the activity sheet on a separate page. All the pages, from each group, can be bound or stapled into a class toy catalogue they can share. Add a front cover. Number the pages and include a contents list.

Developing History
Ages 5–6
© A & C BLACK

Modern or old-fashioned?

Decide whether an object is old or new

- ## Cut out the cards.
- ## Sort them into two groups.

Work in a group.

modern		old-fashioned
 china doll	 remote control car	 wooden duck
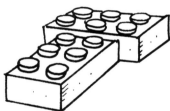 plastic bricks	plastic doll	 water gun
 hobby horse	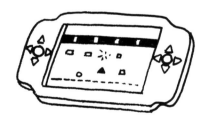 game console	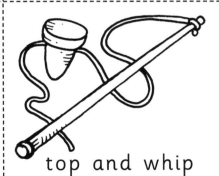 top and whip

Now try this!

- ## Choose one of the toys.
What is it made from?
How does it work?

Teachers' note The children should work together in small groups to sort the cards into two sets. They should take turns to pick a card and place it in a set. The whole group must agree which set each card belongs in. Ask them to explain their decision. If the other children disagree, encourage them to explain why.

Developing History
Ages 5–6
© A & C BLACK

• **Which toys are different from ones we play with today? Colour them in.**

Now try this!

• **Which toys are the same as ones children play with today?**

• **List some other outdoor toys you play with today.**

Teachers' note Discuss with the children the toys in the picture and ensure they all know what they are and how they are played with. Have any of the children played with similar toys? Ask them to tell you when and where. Are there any toys or games that are the same as the ones we play with nowadays? Are there any toys we play with now that are not in the picture?

Developing History
Ages 5–6
© **A & C BLACK**

28

How toys have changed

Describe the characteristics of old and new toys

This teddy bear was made in 1920.

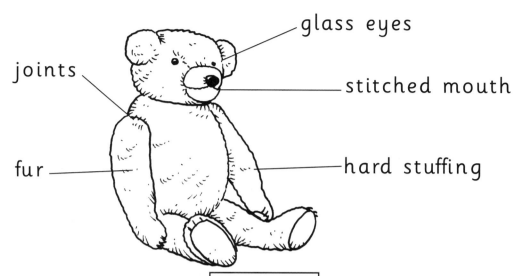

glass eyes

joints

stitched mouth

fur

hard stuffing

- **Draw a picture of a** modern **teddy bear.**
- **Label it.**

Now try this!

- **Talk to a friend about the differences between the two teddies.**

Teachers' note Pictures of teddy bears downloaded from the Internet can provide a selection of visual sources that can be cut out, mounted on card and labelled with captions. Encourage children to think of the materials and technology that were available during the different eras. Allow them to make their own suggestions and offer their own observations.

Developing History
Ages 5–6
© **A & C BLACK**

Museum visit

Investigate the past

- **Use this sheet on a class trip to a** museum.
- **Draw pictures of the toys you see.**
- **Write the name of each toy.**

Baby toys	**Wooden toys**

Metal toys	

- **Use the pictures to make a guidebook.**
- **Design a cover for the book.**

Teachers' note The children should draw pictures of artefacts that take their interest in the correct section of the chart. The fourth box is for the children to choose their own category of toy. Ensure they have written a heading for this category. When producing a guidebook, the children should work in groups. They could print out pictures from the Internet to illustrate and communicate their ideas.

Developing History
Ages 5–6
© A & C BLACK

Snakes and ladders

Find out about the past

- ## This is a game for 2 to 4 players.

Now try this!

- ## What other board games do you know?

Use books or the Internet to help you.

- ## Find out when they were invented.

Teachers' note You will need one copy of this page for up to four children, a dice and counters. Enlarge the page to A3 on a photocopier. Ask the children to find out when the game Snakes and ladders was invented. The extension activity asks them to find out when other popular board games were invented, such as Trivial Pursuit, Monopoly, chess and ludo. They will need access to books and Internet to do this.

Developing History
Ages 5–6
© **A & C BLACK**

Survey

- **Complete this** survey **about the toys people played with.**

1. What toys did you play with when you were a child?

   _____

2. How were they different from toys today?

   _____

3. How were they similar to toys today?

   _____

4. What was your favourite toy?

   _____

5. How old were you when you played with this toy?

   _____

6. Is your favourite toy still popular today?

   _____

7. _____ ?

   _____

8. _____ ?

   _____

Now try this!

- **Tell a friend what you found out.**

Teachers' note Read the questions with the children and make sure they all understand that they are going to investigate what toys were like in the past by asking their parents or grandparents. Explain that interviewing people is a widely used method of gathering historical evidence. Encourage them to add their own questions and ensure they have written them before the sheet is taken home for homework.

Developing History
Ages 5–6
© A & C BLACK

This is my home

Name different types of homes

• Use the word bank to label the homes.

Word bank
caravan
terraced
semi-detached
bungalow
flat
detached

_____   _____

_____

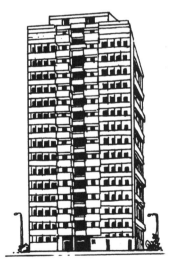

_____   _____

Now try this!

• Draw a picture of your home.

• Complete the sentence.

I live in a _____.

Teachers' note Ask the children to look at the pictures and explain significant features of each one. Ask which are like their homes and which are different. Provide opportunities for the children to discuss aspects of their home with the class. Encourage them to identify features of their own home.

Developing History
Ages 5–6
© A & C BLACK

Looking at houses

Describe and draw details of different features of a home

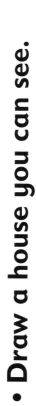

- Draw a house you can see.
- Label the house using the word bank.

Word bank

door
window
chimney
roof
windowsill
letter box
bricks
tiles
thatch
glass
porch
garage

- Compare your drawings with a partner.

Now try this!

34

Teachers' note This sheet is designed to be used on a local class visit where the children can draw a house from observation. It may be wise to get the necessary permissions from the owners of the houses before the trip. The children do not necessarily need to draw the same house but could be split into small groups and observe different houses. Their observations should be discussed within the classroom and their pictures improved to include all key features.

Developing History
Ages 5–6
© A & C BLACK

Houses long ago

Describe the features of a home built a long time ago

This house was built over 100 years ago.

- **Labels as many features as you can.**

Now try this!

- **Compare this house to a picture of a modern house.**

How are they the same?

How are they different?

Teachers' note Ask the children what materials would have been used to build an Edwardian house. Explain that they would not have had the PVC plastic we use today for windows and doors. They would have had wood and glass. They would not have had garages as there were very few cars. Compare to the features they identified in their observations of local homes in the previous activity.

Developing History
Ages 5–6
© **A & C BLACK**

The way things were

Use clues to infer the use of an object

- Look at the old-fashioned pictures.
- Write the names.
- Draw what we use now.

- Choose one of the old-fashioned items.
- Explain how it works.

Now try this!

Teachers' note Before starting the activity sheet, ask the children to use their knowledge about their own homes to identify the objects in the pictures above. Are they the same as today? Which ones do they not recognise? Use the children's ideas and suggestions to build up a word bank of new nouns and adjectives. Ensure all the children know what the objects in the pictures are.

36

Developing History
Ages 5–6
© **A & C BLACK**

Roman baths

Find out about the way of life of people in the more distant past

- ## Cut out the cards.
- ## Match the words to the pictures.

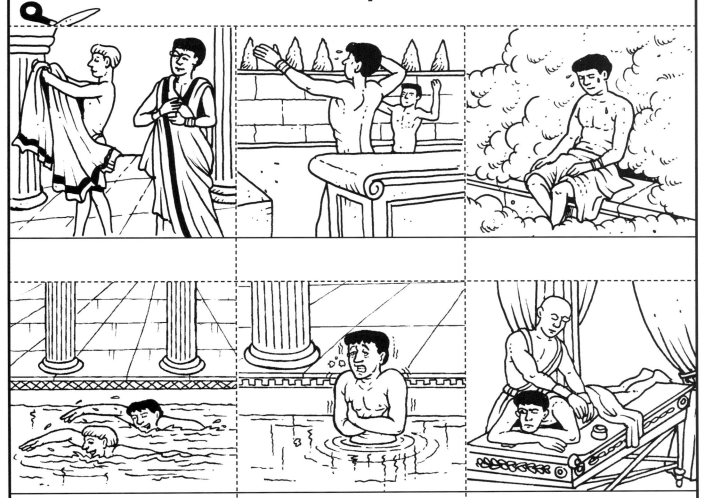

| exercise courtyard | hot room | swimming pool |
| massage room | changing room | cold bath |

- ## Describe your own bath routine.

Developing History
Ages 5–6
© **A & C BLACK**

Pairs: 1

Gain familiarity with artefacts and how they were used

flat iron

washboard

carpet beater

cauldron

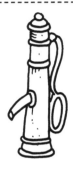

water pump

gas lamp

fireplace

candle

copper kettle

range

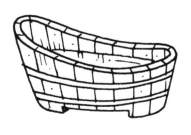

wooden tub

chamber pot

Teachers' note Photocopy pages 38 and 39 onto the same colour card. Give each pair of children one copy of each sheet to play a matching game. Shuffle the cards and spread them out face down on the table. The children take turns to pick up two of the cards, aiming to match an old item and a new one. If they match, they keep them. If they do not, they return them to the table. Encourage the children to role-play using the old-fashioned items.

**Developing History
Ages 5–6**
© **A & C BLACK**

Pairs: 2

Gain familiarity with artefacts and how they were used

iron

washing machine

vacuum cleaner

saucepan

tap

light bulb

radiator

torch

electric kettle

cooker

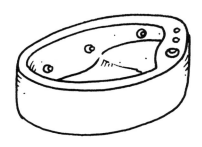

bath

toilet

Teachers' note Use this activity sheet with page 38 to play a matching game. The cards could also be used to play snap.

Developing History
Ages 5–6
© A & C BLACK

39

A day in Victorian life: 1

Communicate aspects of home life in the past

• Cut out the cards. Use them in a role-play.

maid

butler

lady of the house

lord of the house

cook

child

Teachers' note Photocopy the activity sheet onto card. First discuss how living over 100 years ago was different from the way we live today: rich and poor, servants and lords and ladies, household jobs being done at set times (as discussed in the notes on page 8). Organise the class into groups of six. Let each group have a turn in the role-play area with adult support to encourage them to stay in role. Allow the children to role-play several of the characters portrayed on the cards.

Developing History
Ages 5–6
© **A & C BLACK**

A day in Victorian life: 2

Communicate aspects of home life in the past

• **Write a diary page as one of the role-play characters.**

morning _____

_____

_____

_____

afternoon _____

_____

_____

_____

evening _____

_____

_____

_____

Teachers' note The children should choose one of the characters from page 40 and complete the diary page in role as that character. Use the activity sheet to communicate what they have learnt through their role-play in words and pictures. Encourage them to think of the day divided into morning, afternoon and evening and to use this vocabulary related to periods of time correctly.

Developing History
Ages 5–6
© A & C BLACK

Holidays today

- **Colour the seaside picture.**

- **Make a list of the activities shown in the picture.**

_____   _____

_____   _____

_____   _____

- **Which would be your favourite thing to do?**

_____

Now try this!

- **Name a seaside town you have been to.**
- **Find it on a map.**

Teachers' note Discuss the picture on the activity sheet. Help the children to find clues to show them what sort of holiday is shown. Ask if anyone has been on a seaside holiday or day trip to the seaside. Where did they go? What did they do? Locate the places they have visited on maps and globes.

Developing History
Ages 5–6
© A & C BLACK

Holiday snaps

Distinguish between holidays in the recent and more distant past

• **Cut out the cards. Put the pictures in order from** [past] **to** [present]**.**

• **Match the captions to the pictures.**

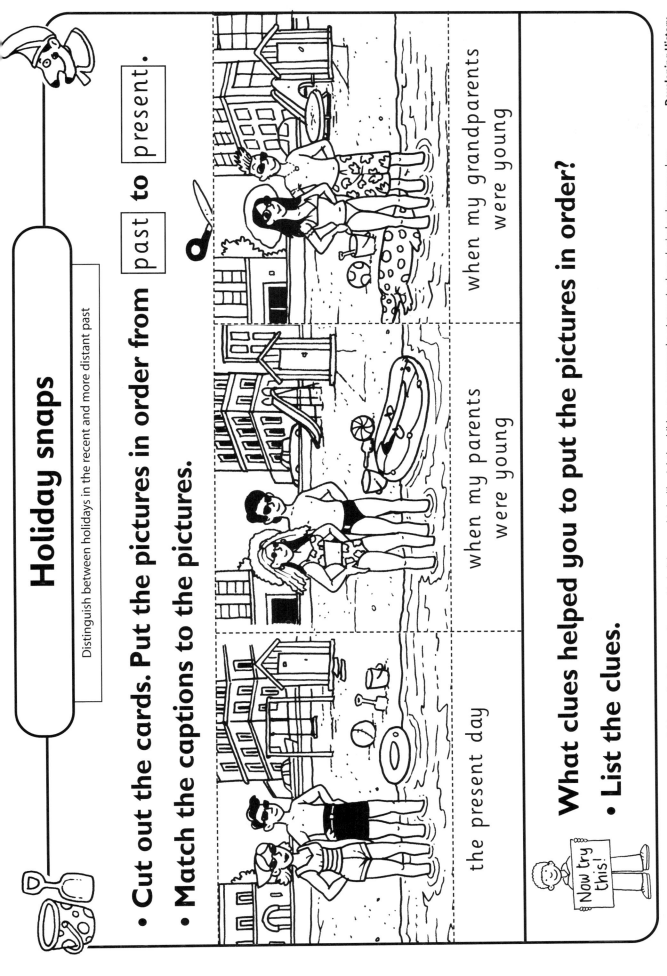

when my grandparents were young

when my parents were young

the present day

What clues helped you to put the pictures in order?

• **List the clues.**

Now try this!

Teachers' note Discuss the pictures. Help the children to find clues to what seaside holidays used to be like. Ask the children to sequence the pictures in chronological order: now; when parents/carers were young; when grandma/granddad were young. Talk about the clues they used to help in sequencing, e.g. clothes, hairstyles, amusements, vehicles, buildings. Use the discussion to reinforce time-related vocabulary.

Developing History
Ages 5–6
© A & C BLACK

Trip to the sea

Recognise some things change and others stay the same

- ## Which things are similar in the pictures?
- ## Which things are different? List them.

Today

Long ago

Similar things

_____
_____
_____
_____
_____

Different things

_____
_____
_____
_____
_____

Now try this!

- ## Share your ideas with a friend.

Teachers' note Ask the children to look carefully at the pictures. Are there any cars? Are there ice cream sellers? Are there families on the beach? Are there people wearing swimsuits? Ask the children to identify and write down three things that are similar in the photographs and three that are different. Provide opportunities for the children to discuss and share their ideas.

Developing History
Ages 5–6
© **A & C BLACK**

In times gone by

Communicate knowledge of seaside holidays from the more distant past

- **Imagine you are a Victorian on a seaside holiday. Write a postcard to a friend.**

POST CARD

POSTAGE
E ONE PENNY L

Teachers' note The children should first complete the activity on page 44. Encourage the children to write a message on the postcard frame describing their Victorian seaside holiday. The front and back of the postcard could be cut out and glued back-to-back for display within the classroom. Discuss the penny black stamp and its importance.

Developing History
Ages 5–6
© A & C BLACK

45

Mementoes

• **Label the seaside** souvenirs.

A souvenir is something that reminds you of your holiday.

• **What do the souvenirs tell us about seaside holidays in the past? Talk with a friend.**

Now try this!

• **How are these souvenirs different to the ones we buy today?**

Teachers' note This activity sheet should be enlarged onto A3 paper. Talk about the souvenirs that can be seen in the shop window. Discuss what they are. How would they remind you of a seaside holiday? What sorts of things have the children bought on a seaside holiday? List the things they have bought. Why are these souvenirs important to the children?

Developing History
Ages 5–6
© A & C BLACK

Punch and Judy

Understand some things change over time and some things stay the same

• **Cut out the Punch and Judy characters.**
Use them to help you make up a story.

That's the way to do it.

Punch

Judy

baby

crocodile

policeman

sausages

Now try this!

• **Act out your Punch and Judy stories.**

Teachers' note Begin with a preliminary discussion on how Punch and Judy shows have changed over the years. Ask how many children have seen a Punch and Judy show and talk about the characters. Discuss possible storylines. Ask what would happen if Punch dropped the baby out of the window? What would happen if Punch was arrested? What would happen if Punch stole the sausages and blamed Judy? The children should work in small groups.

Developing History
Ages 5–6
© A & C BLACK

Super-fan facts

- **Choose a** famous **person.**

_____

- **Draw or stick on a picture.**
- **Write four facts about them.**

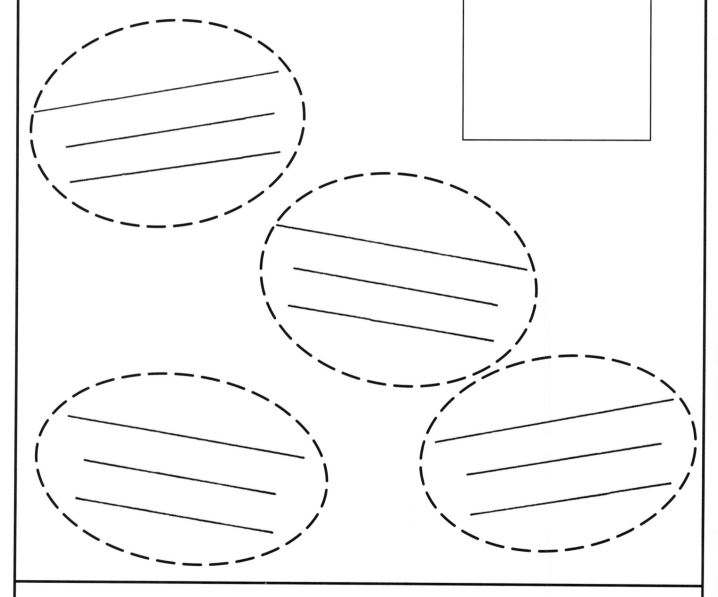

- **Write a sentence to explain why the person is famous.**

Teachers' note With the class, look up the word 'famous' in a dictionary. Talk about famous people the children know, both alive and dead. List them on the board. Let them choose their own famous person to complete the activity sheet. Remind them what a fact is, and discuss examples.

Developing History
Ages 5–6
© A & C BLACK

48

Pocahontas

Recount main events

- **Cut out the sentences.**
- **Put them in the correct order.**

A colony is a group of people who settle in a new country.

In 1614, Pocahontas married John Rolfe and a year later had a son called Thomas.

They went to England in 1616 and Pocahontas met James I to raise support for the Jamestown colony.

Settlers from England arrived in Virginia in May 1607 and started a colony called Jamestown.

Pocahontas was captured by the settlers, but was treated kindly.

Pocahontas died of a European illness on the ship home.

Pocahontas took food to the settlers and traded with them.

She saved John Smith's life.

She was baptised in 1613 and re-named Rebecca.

Now try this!

- **Draw a scene from the story.**

Teachers' note Read the sentences with the children. Discuss what the children know about Pocahontas before they attempt ordering the sentences. When they have finished ordering the sentences, ask why they decided to put the sentences in the order they have. The sentences could also be used as captions for the children's own pictures, which could be displayed as a class storyboard.

Developing History
Ages 5–6
© **A & C BLACK**

49

The Pocahontas legend

Recount an episode from a story from the past

- **Listen to the story of how John Smith and Pocahontas met.**

- **Talk with a friend about what is happening in the pictures.**

- **Write a sentence to explain how Pocahontas saved John Smith's life.**

- **Complete the sentence.**

Pocahontas is famous because _____.

Now try this!

Teachers' note Read out the story of how John Smith and Pocahontas met (see pages 9–10). Provide plenty of opportunity for discussion. Encourage the children to think about why Pocahontas is famous. Tell the children she acted as a go-between for her people and the new colonists and saving John Smith made her a heroine. Emphasise how she was known for her courage and kindness because she took food to the settlers and traded with them.

Developing History
Ages 5–6
© A & C BLACK

50

Identify reasons for actions

- **Tick the reasons why Pocahontas went to England.**

Because she liked ships. ☐

To get support for Jamestown. ☐

To help England and North America become friends. ☐

To go to a party. ☐

Now try this!

- **What sort of person was Pocahontas?**

Pocahontas was _____

_____.

Teachers' note The children should first complete the activity on page 49. Ask how they would feel if they had to travel a long way to a place they had never seen before. List their ideas. Explain journeys in the past used to take longer and were dangerous. Ask them why they think King James I wanted to meet Pocahontas. Discuss how strange England would have seemed to Pocahontas. Allow time for the children to report back their ideas in small groups.

Developing History
Ages 5–6
© **A & C BLACK**

Tutankhamun

Infer information from secondary sources

- **Draw Tutankhamun's clothes.**
- **Look at pictures to help you.**

As a pharaoh, he was the most powerful person in ancient Egypt.

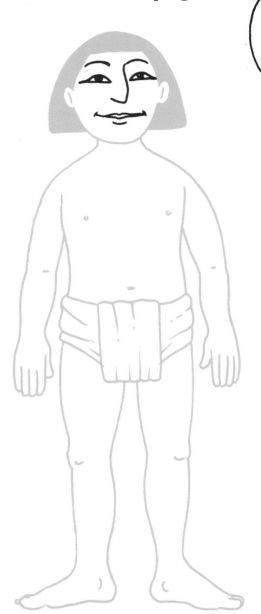

- **Tell a friend how Tutankhamun's clothes are different from those worn by royalty today.**

Teachers' note Before the lesson begins, ensure you have enough books, websites and pictures of Tutankhamun for the children to study. Point out the clothes he wears, his headdress, loincloth, collar and make-up. Provide time for the children to share what they found out about Tutankhamun's clothes from their research and show their pictures.

Developing History
Ages 5–6
© A & C BLACK

Making a mummy

- **Cut out the cards.**
- **Put them in order.**

A mummy is a body wrapped in bandages.

The coffins are placed in a sarcophagus.

The mummy is lowered into two wooden coffins.

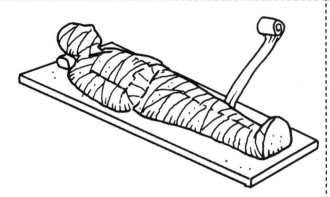

The body is wrapped in bandages.

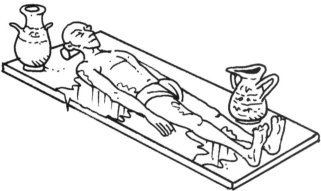

The body is washed with wine and rinsed with water from the River Nile.

Now try this!

- **Draw Tutankhamun's sarcophagus.**

A sarcophagus is a coffin made of stone.

Teachers' note Discuss the mummification process with the children using the pictures and their captions as prompts. Give the children time to look at the pictures. Afterwards, show them the correct order the mummification process should be sequenced in. This could be done by preparing a sheet enlarged to A3 or projected on an interactive whiteboard.

Developing History
Ages 5–6
© A & C BLACK

53

Uncovering the tomb

Identify how people became famous

Use books and the Internet to find out.

- **Explain what happened before and after Tutankhamun's tomb was discovered.**

Before

After

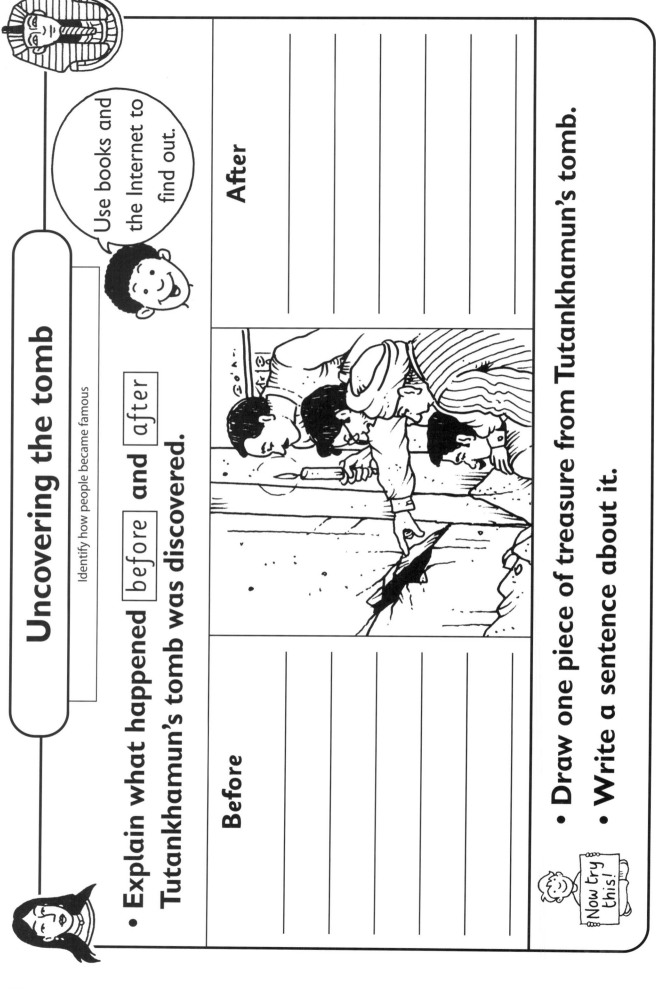

Now try this!

- **Draw one piece of treasure from Tutankhamun's tomb.**
- **Write a sentence about it.**

54

Teachers' note Encourage the children to talk about what they see in the picture. Allow time for the children to role-play discovering the tomb. They should fill in what happened before the tomb was found and what happened after. Explain how long it took Lord Carnarvon and Howard Carter to find the tomb and they were about to give up looking. Tell the children it was unusual to find such an intact tomb, as many had been broken into and the treasures stolen. This treasure provided historians with lots of important information about the ancient Egyptians.

Developing History
Ages 5–6
© A & C BLACK

Brunel's achievements

Isambard Kingdom Brunel was a famous engineer.

- **Label Brunel's designs.**

Great _____

_____

_____

_____

Word bank

Clifton Suspension
    Bridge
Great Western
    Railway
Paddington Station
SS Great Eastern

Now try this!

You are to travel on Brunel's railway.

- **Find London and Bristol on a map.**

- **List the towns the Great Western Railway travelled through.**

Teachers' note Emphasise the wide variety of Brunel's achievements and designs. Ask what contribution these designs have made to people's way of life. Has it been an important contribution? Why? List their ideas and suggestions. The children will need access to books or the Internet for the extension activity. A useful website is www.bbc.co.uk.

Developing History
Ages 5–6
© **A & C BLACK**

Brunel's designs

Find out about the way of life of people in the more distant past

• Look at the picture of the SS Great Britain. Write the labels.

Word bank

mast
rudder
funnel
iron hull
front sail
propeller

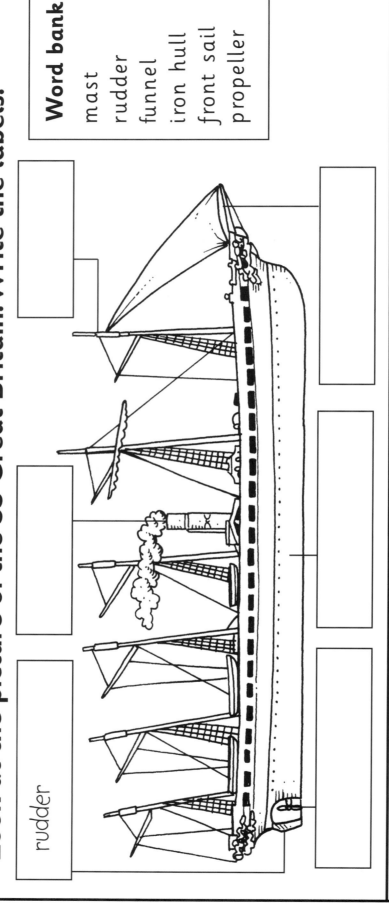

rudder

• What other ships did Brunel design?
Use books and the Internet to find out.

Now try this!

Teachers' note Make sure the children understand all the terms in the word bank before they start the activity. Explain to the children that the SS *Great Britain* was the second ship Brunel invented but the first steam ship.

Developing History
Ages 5–6
© **A & C BLACK**

• **Draw or stick on a picture of a** [modern] **ship.**

Modern ship	Victorian steam ship

What are the differences?

_____

_____

_____

_____

What are the similarities?

_____

_____

_____

_____

Now try this!

What [new] **features can you see?**

• **Complete the sentence.**

I can see _____.

Teachers' note The children should first complete the activities on pages 55 and 56. Have a selection of pictures of modern cruise liners from travel brochures and the Internet for the children to cut up and compare to the SS *Great Britain*. Brainstorm the differences as a preliminary class discussion. List their suggestions.

Developing History
Ages 5–6
© A & C BLACK

Guy Fawkes

Describe clothes worn a long time ago

- ## Look at what Guy Fawkes is wearing.

- ## Write a sentence to describe Guy Fawkes' clothes.

_____

_____

_____

_____

_____ .

- ## How are they different to clothes worn by men today?

_____

_____

_____

_____

Now try this!

- ## Learn the rhyme 'Remember, remember the fifth of November.'

Teachers' note Read the rhyme from the notes on the activities on page 11 and discuss with the children. Have a selection of pictures available of Guy Fawkes and modern men's clothes from mail order catalogues. Look in detail at Guy Fawkes' clothes and hair and compare to pictures of what men look like and wear today. Encourage the children to highlight differences and similarities.

Developing History
Ages 5–6
© A & C BLACK